GREAT MINDS® WIT & WISDOM

Grade 2 Module 1:
A Season of Change

Student Edition

Table of Contents

Handout 22B: Change Cards

Handout 22C: Multiple-Choice Questions

Handout 23A: Word Link-Up

Handout 23B: Informative Paragraph Cards

Handout 23C: Conjunction Review

Handout 23D: Mix and Mingle Compound Sentence Cards

Handout 24A: Informative Writing Checklist

Handout 25A: Notice and Wonder Chart

Handout 25B: Artist's Colors

Handout 25C: Fluency Homework

Handout 26A: Revision Paragraph

Handout 27A: Sky Tree Timeline

Handout 27B: Revision Paragraph and Checklist

Handout 28A: Season Trees

Handout 28B: Matching Key Terms

Handout 29A: Informative Paragraph Parts Cards

Handout 29B: Informative Writing Checklist

Handout 30A: Evidence Organizer

Handout 31A: Informative Writing Checklist

Handout 31B: Evidence Organizer

Volume of Reading Reflection Questions

Wit & Wisdom Parent Tip Sheet

Name:

Handout 1A: Fluency Homework

Dear Parents,

Welcome to our classroom! This year your child will be receiving regular reading fluency practice for homework. Fluency homework helps build your child's confidence with reading.

Each week of fluency homework, your child has a passage of text upon which to focus.

On the first homework assignment with a new passage, we want students to be able to say every word clearly and to know what the passage means. If they accomplish just that much, please check off the expectation.

On the second assignment, we want students to chunk the words as they read. We all do this when we speak! The easiest way to do this is to read to a comma or a period. For poems, this means reading the lines as if they had a comma or period. We encourage you to read aloud with your child and to play with the phrasing.

The third day might be the most fun. Encourage your child to be dramatic and theatrical! Choose the words that carry the deepest meaning for emphasis. Say those words more boldly, being sure to continue the phrasing.

On weeks when there is a fourth and fifth assignment, everything gets pulled together. This might be a chance for your child to call a grandparent or perform for the dog and cat! We want your child to read so that everyone understands the words, hears the words, and understands the meaning from the way the text was read.

You are a very important member of our teaching team. Please let me know if there is any way I can help you.

Sincerely,

Name:

Handout 1A: Fluency Homework: Option A

Dot a dot dot dot a dot dot

Spotting the windowpane.

Spack a spack speck flick a flack fleck

Freckling the windowpane.

A spatter a scatter a wet cat a clatter

A splatter a rumble outside.

Merriam, Eve. "Weather," *Catch a Little Rhyme:* Macmillan, 1966

36 words

Have an adult initial each day that you read the passage three to five times. Optional: Have a peer sign on the second row of boxes, checking your progress.

Day 1	Day 2	Day 3

Student Performance Checklist:

Read easily without stumbling.

Read with appropriate phrasing and pausing.

Read with appropriate expression for the selection.

Read at a good pace, not too fast and not too slow.

Read to be heard and understood.

Teacher Notes:

Name:

Handout 1A: Fluency Homework: Option B

Slosh a galosh slosh a galosh

Slither and slather a glide

A puddle a jump a puddle a jump

A puddle a jump puddle splosh

A juddle a pump a luddle a dump

A pudmuddle jump in and slide!

Merriam, Eve. "Weather," Catch a Little Rhyme: Macmillan, 1966

39 words

Have an adult initial each day that you read the passage three to five times. Optional: Have a peer sign on the second row of boxes, checking your progress.

Day 1	Day 2	Day 3

Student Performance Checklist:

Read easily without stumbling.

Read with appropriate phrasing and pausing.

Read with appropriate expression for the selection.

Read at a good pace, not too fast and not too slow.

Read to be heard and understood.

Teacher Notes:

Name:_____

Handout 2A: Artist's Colors

Directions: Use crayons to color the palette and show what colors the artist used in the painting.

I added the color_____

because_____

_____

I added the color_____

because_____

_____

Why did the artist choose to use those colors?
_____
_____
_____

I added the color_____

because_____

What season does this painting show?

_____

I added the color_____

because_____

_____

I added the color_____

because_____

_____

Name: _____

Handout 2B: Change Chart for "Weather"

Directions: Fill in the chart with examples of what changes happen at the beginning, middle, and end of "Weather." Then, use information from the Change Chart to answer the question below.

What happens in "Weather"?		
Beginning	Middle	End

<u>Focusing Question:</u>

What changes in "Weather"? _____

_____

_____

_____

Name:

Handout 3A: Fluency Key Words

Directions: *Circle which reader you are. Then underline the words you will emphasize as you read. Review the chart below and practice reading the poem fluently with your group.*

Dot a dot dot dot a dot dot

Spotting the windowpane.

Reader 1 (lines 1–4)

Spack a spack speck flick a flack fleck

Freckling the windowpane.

A spatter a scatter a wet cat a clatter

A splatter a rumble outside.

Umbrella umbrella umbrella umbrella

Bumbershoot barrel of rain.

Reader 2 (lines 5–10)

Slosh a galosh slosh a galosh

Slither and slather a glide.

A puddle a jump a puddle a jump

A puddle a jump puddle splosh.

A juddle a pump a luddle a dump

A pudmuddle jump in and slide!

Reader 3 (lines 11–14)

Fluency Reminders		Evaluation
Criteria	Did you...	
Accuracy ✔	I read without any mistakes.	
Phrasing	I paid attention to punctuation and spaces between lines. I read information in meaningful chunks.	
Rate	I read at the appropriate speed—not too fast and not too slow.	
Expression	I read words with emotion or feeling.	
Performance	I articulated words clearly and read loudly enough for my audience to hear.	

Name:

Handout 3B: Fluency Self-Reflection

Directions: Think about your reading of the poem and answer the questions below.

A = I **always** did that.   S = I **sometimes** did that.

N = I'll do that next time.

Fluency Reminders		Evaluation
Criteria	Did you...	
Accuracy ✔	I read without any mistakes.	
Phrasing 66 99 •••	I paid attention to punctuation and spaces between lines. I read information in meaningful chunks.	
Rate	I read at the appropriate speed— not too fast and not too slow.	
Expression ☺ ☹	I read words with emotion or feeling.	
Performance	I articulated words clearly and read loudly enough for my audience to hear.	

I am most proud of_____
in my fluency.

I want to work on_____
in my fluency.

Name:

Handout 3C: Fluency Self-Reflection

Directions: Think about your reading of the poem and answer the questions below.

A = I always did that.   S = I sometimes did that.

N = I'll do that next time.

Expectation	Evaluation
My voice pauses and stops in places, especially where there is a new stanza or end of a line.	
The volume of my voice increases and decreases.	
My voice has expression and sounds like a person who is talking.	
My voice goes faster and slower in different places.	
My voice shows that I understand what the text says. I get louder when I say "Bumbershoot."	
I emphasize important words.	

I am most proud of_____
in my fluendy.

I want to work on_____
in my fluency.

Name:

Handout 4A: Sample Informative Paragraph 1

Directions: Cut along the dotted lines and distribute the strips. Then read and order to create an informative paragraph.

Question: What do people do outside in the fall?

Playing sports, like football, is another fall activity.

When the leaves fall off the trees, raking and jumping into piles of leaves is fun.

There are lots of outdoor activities to enjoy in fall.

Some people enjoy picking apples and pumpkins in the fall.

Name: _____

Handout 4B: Fluency Homework Option A

Directions: Practice reading the passage daily for homework. Have an adult initial the bottom after you have done the reading.

In some areas, the air gets cooler in fall. There is less sunlight at this time of year. The days become shorter as the sun goes down earlier each night. Fall can be windy and chilly. We wear pants, sweaters, and coats to stay warm.

Herrington, Lisa. *How Do You Know It's Fall?* New York: Scholastic, 2014. 9–10. Print.

45 words

Have an adult initial each day that you read the passage three to five times. Optional: Have a peer sign on the second row of boxes, checking your progress.

Day 1	Day 2	Day 3

Student Performance Checklist:

Read easily without stumbling.

Read with appropriate phrasing and pausing.

Read with appropriate expression for the selection.

Read at a good pace, not too fast and not too slow.

Read to be heard and understood.

Teacher Notes:

Name: _____

Handout 4B: Fluency Homework Option B

Directions: Practice reading the passage daily for homework. Have an adult initial the bottom after you have done the reading.

Animals use this time to get ready for winter. Many store food for the cold weather ahead. Squirrels hide nuts and acorns. Some birds migrate. They leave for warmer winter homes. You might hear a flock of geese honking in the sky. Monarch butterflies also migrate. They journey to warmer places during the cold winter months Herrington, Lisa. *How Do You Know It's Fall?* New York: Scholastic, 2014. 14–19. Print. <div align="right">**56 words**</div>
Have an adult initial each day that you read the passage three to five times. Optional: Have a peer sign on the second row of boxes, checking your progress.

Day 1	Day 2	Day 3

Student Performance Checklist:

Read easily without stumbling.

Read with appropriate phrasing and pausing.

Read with appropriate expression for the selection.

Read at a good pace, not too fast and not too slow.

Read to be heard and understood.

Teacher Notes:

Name:

Handout 4B: Fluency Homework Option C

Directions: Practice reading the passage daily for homework. Have an adult initial the bottom after you have done the reading.

Many crops are ready to be eaten in fall. We can pick ripe apples from trees. Yum! Apples are crunchy and sweet. In October, we pick pumpkins from a patch. We carve them into jack-o'-lanterns. On Halloween, we dress up in costumes. We go trick-or-treating. In late November, we celebrate another fall holiday—Thanksgiving. We eat a big turkey meal with our family. We give thanks for all the good things in our lives.

Herrington, Lisa. *How Do You Know It's Fall?* New York: Scholastic, 2014. 21–25. Print.

74 words

Have an adult initial each day that you read the passage three to five times. Optional: Have a peer sign on the second row of boxes, checking your progress.

Day 1	Day 2	Day 3

Student Performance Checklist:

Read easily without stumbling.

Read with appropriate phrasing and pausing.

Read with appropriate expression for the selection.

Read at a good pace, not too fast and not too slow.

Read to be heard and understood.

Teacher Notes:

Name:

Handout 5A: Key Terms

Directions: First predict the chapter where you will find the Key Term by using the table of contents. Later, confirm your prediction by finding the word in the text as you read and write the chapter number in the column under "Find the chapter."

Key Terms	Predict the chapter.	Find the chapter.	
cooler			
migrate			
store			
ripe			
celebrate			

Name: _____

Handout 5B: Main Idea and Details Chart

Cut on dotted lines.

Name:

Cut on dotted lines.

Name:

Directions: This handout will be used for several lessons. Use this chart to keep track of the main topic and details and the page number where the information is found.

Pages:	Main Topic and Details

Name:

Handout 5C: Informative Writing Anchor Chart

Directions: Use this chart to organize your thoughts about informative writing.

Part of Paragraph	What It Does	How You Use
T = Topic Statement	Tells the essential idea	• Answers the question. • Comes near the beginning. • States the essential idea.

Name:

Handout 5D: Sample Informative Paragraph 2

Directions: This paragraph is missing a topic statement. Read the paragraph, determine the essential meaning of the paragraph, and then draft two possible topic statements for the paragraph.

Some animals fly away to warmer places. Monarch butterflies

fly to Mexico! Squirrels collect food for winter. They hide nuts

and acorns so they have enough food during the winter.

I think the essential meaning of this paragraph is:

Topic Statement:

Topic Statement:

Name:

Handout 6A: Sample Informative Paragraph 3

Directions: Read the paragraph. Determine the essential meaning of the paragraph. Then draft two possible topic statements for the paragraph.

In October, Halloween is a fun holiday. Kids carve pumpkins and dress up in costumes for trick-or-treating. Then comes Thanksgiving. This holiday is a time for lots of food and family!

I think the essential meaning of this paragraph is:

Topic Statement:

Topic Statement:

Name:

Handout 7A: Main Topic of Text

Directions: Use this chart to help you understand main topics of text.

Pages	Main Topics	
8–11		Weather in fall gets chilly.
14–19		Animals get ready for winter in fall.
21–25		Kids do fun things in fall.
All		

Name:

Handout 7B: Subjects

Directions: Underline the verbs in these sentences.

PART I

1. Leaves change colors.

2. Birds fly south.

3. Children like to run through fallen leaves.

4. Each season lasts about four months.

5. We wear pants, sweaters, and coats to stay warm.

6. Fall bursts with color.

7. Some leaves turn red, orange, yellow, and brown. Then they drop off the trees.

8. Squirrels hide nuts and acorns.

9. Some birds migrate.

PART II

10. They leave for warmer winter homes.

11. Monarch butterflies also migrate.

12. They journey to warmer places during the cold winter months.

13. We can pick ripe apples from the tree.

14. Apples are crunchy and sweet.

15. We rake leaves into piles.

Name:

Handout 9A: Knowledge Journal Questions

Directions: Refer to these questions as you do a Gallery Walk.

Knowledge Journal Questions

Text: How *Do You Know It's Fall?*

Focusing Question: How does the change in fall weather impact people and nature?

- What did you learn about change?

- What did you learn about fall?

- What did you learn about plants and animals?

- What did you learn about the impact of changes in fall?

- What did you learn about informational text?

- What did you learn about reading informational text?

- What did you learn about main ideas and details?

- What did you learn about words and how they work?

- What did you learn about informative paragraphs?

- What did you learn about topic sentences?

- What did you learn about Evidence Charts?

- What did you learn about Socratic Seminars?

- What new words did you learn?

- What did you learn about reading fluently?

Name:

Handout 9B: Socratic Seminar Self-Reflection

Directions: Reflect on the Socratic Seminar and mark **A** for always, **S** for sometimes or **N** for next time.

A = I always did that.   S = I sometimes did that.

N = I'll do that next time.

Expectation	Evaluation (A, S, N)
I noticed the whole message.	
I linked what I said to what others said.	
I looked at the speaker.	
I spoke only when no one else was speaking.	
I used kind words.	

Name:

Handout 10A: Notice and Wonder Chart

Directions: Jot down observations and questions about how the Little Yellow Leaf changes in the Notice and Wonder columns.

Notice	**Wonder**
To see or observe	To ask questions

Name:

Handout 10B: Fluency Homework Option A

Directions: Practice reading the passage daily for homework. Have an adult initial the bottom after you have done the reading.

It was autumn. In the hush of the forest a lone yellow leaf clung to the branch of a great oak tree. *I'm not ready yet,* thought the Little Yellow Leaf as a riot of fiery leaves chased and swirled round the tree.

Berger, Carin. *The Little Yellow Leaf*, New York: Greenwillow Books, 2008, 23–24. Print.

43 words

Have an adult initial each day that you read the passage three to five times. Optional: Have a peer sign on the second row of boxes, checking your progress.

Day 1	Day 2	Day 3

Student Performance Checklist:

Read easily without stumbling.

Read with appropriate phrasing and pausing.

Read with appropriate expression for the selection.

Read at a good pace, not too fast and not too slow.

Read to be heard and understood.

Teacher Notes:

Name:

Handout 10B: Fluency Homework Option B

Directions: Practice reading the passage daily for homework. Have an adult initial the bottom after you have done the reading.

"You're here?" called the Little Yellow Leaf.

"I am," said the Little Scarlet Leaf.

"Like me!" said the Little Yellow Leaf.

Neither Spoke. Finally...

"Will you?" asked the Little Yellow Leaf.

"I will!" said the Little Scarlet Leaf.

And one, two, three, they let go and soared. Into the waiting wind they danced...

off and away and away and away.
Together.

61 words

Berger, Carin. *The Little Yellow Leaf*, New York: Greenwillow Books, 2008, 23–24. Print.

Have an adult initial each day that you read the passage three to five times. Optional: Have a peer sign on the second row of boxes, checking your progress.

Day 1	Day 2	Day 3

Student Performance Checklist:

Read easily without stumbling.

Read with appropriate phrasing and pausing.

Read with appropriate expression for the selection.

Read at a good pace, not too fast and not too slow.

Read to be heard and understood.

Teacher Notes:

Name:

Handout 11A: Reader's Theater Script

Adapted from *The Little Yellow Leaf* by Carin Berger, pages 23–25

Directions: Read through the script. As a group, decide which person will read which part. Underline your part wherever it appears on the script. Practice with your group.

Cast:

- Little Yellow Leaf

- Narrator 1

- Little Scarlet Leaf

- Narrator 2

Little Yellow Leaf: *You're here?*

Narrator 1:   *Called the Little Yellow Leaf.*

Little Scarlet Leaf: *I am,*

Narrator 2:   *Called the Little Scarlet Leaf.*

Narrator 1:   *Neither spoke.*

Narrator 2:   *Finally...*

Little Scarlet Leaf: *Will you?*

Narrator 1:   *Asked the Little Scarlet Leaf.*

Little Yellow Leaf: *I will!*

Narrator 2:   *Said the Little Yellow Leaf.*

All together: *And one, two, three, they let go and soared.*

Name:

Handout 11B: Exemplar Paragraph

Directions: Identify the topic statement and evidence statements in the exemplar paragraph. Use green, yellow, and blue colored pencils to underline the sentences.

The tree changes from late fall to winter. At first it's fall and most of the leaves are brown and orange and are on the ground. Then the apples grow musky and ripe and the leaves on the ground get dry and crackly. Finally, the branches are completely bare and covered with a shimmer of snow.

Name:

Handout 11C: Change Chart for *The Little Yellow Leaf*

Directions: Fill in the chart with sketches of what changes happen at the beginning middle, and end of The Little Yellow Leaf.

What happens in *The Little Yellow Leaf?*		
Beginning	Middle	End

Name:

Handout 13A: Informative Writing Checklist

Directions: Complete this checklist after completing your informative paragraph. Mark + for "yes" and Δ for "not yet." Be sure to include a writing goal.

Grade 2 Informative Writing Checklist		
	Self +/ Δ	Teacher +/ Δ
Reading Comprehension		
I understand how the Little Yellow Leaf changes.		
Structure		
I introduce the topic with a topic statement.		
I include at least three sentences with evidence.		
I use sequencing words: *first*, *then*, and *finally* in the correct order.		
Development		
My evidence relates to the topic and helps develop my points.		
Style		
I use words that are about the topic.		
I use adjectives in my writing.		

Conventions		
Every sentence has a subject and a verb.		
Total # of checks		

My writing goal is_____

_____

_____

Teacher Feedback

Name:

Handout 15A: Notice and Wonder Chart

Directions: Jot down observations and questions about how the chameleon changes in the Notice and Wonder columns.

 **Notice** To see or observe	 **Wonder** To ask questions

Name:

Handout 15B: Fluency Homework Option A

Directions: Practice reading the passages daily for homework. Have an adult initial the bottom after you have done the reading.

Parrots are green, goldfish are red, elephants are gray, pigs are pink. All animals have a color of their own except for chameleons. They change color wherever they go. On lemons they are yellow. In the heather they are purple. And on the tiger they are striped like tigers.

One day a chameleon who was sitting on a tiger's tail said to himself, "If I remain on a leaf I shall be green forever, and so I too will have a color of my own."

Print.84 words

Lionni, Leo. *A Color of His Own*, New York: Dragonfly Books, 1975, 1–12.

Have an adult initial each day that you read the passage three to five times. Optional: Have a peer sign on the second row of boxes, checking your progress.

Day 1	Day 2	Day 3

Student Performance Checklist:

Read easily without stumbling.

Read with appropriate phrasing and pausing.

Read with appropriate expression for the selection.

Read at a good pace, not too fast and not too slow.

Read to be heard and understood.

Teacher Notes:

Name:

Handout 15B: Fluency Homework Option B

Directions: Practice reading the passage daily for homework. Have an adult initial the bottom after you have done the reading.

And so they remained side by side.
They were green together
and purple
and yellow
and red with white polka dots. And they lived happily ever after.
67 words
Lionni, Leo. A Color of His Own, New York: Dragonfly Books, 1975, 23–28. Print.

Have an adult initial each day that you read the passage three to five times. Optional: Have a peer sign on the second row of boxes, checking your progress.

Day 1	Day 2	Day 3

Student Performance Checklist:

Read easily without stumbling.

Read with appropriate phrasing and pausing.

Read with appropriate expression for the selection.

Read at a good pace, not too fast and not too slow.

Read to be heard and understood.

Teacher Notes:

Name: _____

Handout 16A: Story Elements

Directions: Select the correct answer to each question.

1. Who is the main character in *A Color of His Own?*

   A. The older, wiser chameleon

   B. The chameleon who wants a color of his own

   C. The tiger

   D. All of the above

2. What is the setting of *A Color of His Own?*

   A. Outside on a tree

   B. Outside in autumn

   C. Outside in winter

   D. All of the above

Name:

Handout 18A: Informative Writing Checklist

Directions: Complete this checklist after completing your informative paragraph. Be sure to include a writing goal.

Grade 2 Informative Writing Checklist		
	Self +/ Δ	Teacher +/ Δ
Reading Comprehension		
I understand how the Little Yellow Leaf changes.		
Structure		
I introduce the topic with a topic statement.		
I include at least three sentences with evidence.		
I use sequencing words: *first, then*, and *finally* in the correct order.		
Development		
My evidence relates to the topic and helps develop my points.		
Style		
I use words that are about the topic.		
I use adjectives in my writing.		
Conventions		
Every sentence has a subject and a verb.		

Total # of checks		

My writing goal is_____

_____

_____

Teacher Feedback

Name:

Handout 19A: Socratic Seminar Self-Reflection

Directions: Reflect on the Socratic Seminar and mark *A* for always, *S* for sometimes or *N* for next time.

A = I always did that.   S = I sometimes did that.

N = I'll do that next time.

Expectation	Evaluation (A, S, N)
I noticed the whole message.	
I linked what I said to what others said.	
I looked at the speaker.	
I spoke only when no one else was speaking.	
I used kind words.	

Name:

Handout 20A: Notice and Wonder Chart

Directions: Jot down observations and questions about *Why Do Leaves Change Color?* in the Notice and Wonder columns.

 **Notice** To pay attention; to see	 **Wonder** To ask questions

Name:

Handout 20B: Fluency Homework Option A

Directions: Practice reading the passage daily for homework. Have an adult initial the bottom after you have done the reading.

Just a few weeks ago, all the leaves were green. Back in the spring, the tiny new leaves uncurled from their buds.

The green color in the leaves helps them to absorb or hold sunlight. Chlorophyll gives the leaves their green coloring. Chlorophyll is a natural coloring called a pigment.

50 words

Maestro, Betsy. *Why Do Leaves Change Color?* New York: HarperCollins, 1994. 9. Print.

Have an adult initial each day that you read the passage three to five times. Optional: Have a peer sign on the second row of boxes, checking your progress.

Day 1	Day 2	Day 3	Day 4

Student Performance Checklist:

Read easily without stumbling.

Read with appropriate phrasing and pausing.

Read with appropriate expression for the selection.

Read at a good pace, not too fast and not too slow.

Read to be heard and understood.

Teacher Notes:

Name:

Handout 20B: Fluency Homework Option B

Directions: Practice reading the passage daily for homework. Have an adult initial the bottom after you have done the reading.

Leaves are very important to the tree. They make a kind of sugar that is the tree's food. Leaves need sunlight, water, and air to make this food.

The leaves work to feed the tree all summer long. The sugar is used by all parts of the tree—the leaves, branches, trunk, and roots. The food, or sugar, helps the tree to grow. Extra sugar is stored in the leaves.

70 words

Maestro, Betsy. *Why Do Leaves Change Color?* New York: HarperCollins, 1994. 11. Print.

Have an adult initial each day that you read the passage three to five times. Optional: Have a peer sign on the second row of boxes, checking your progress.

Day 1	Day 2	Day 3	Day 4

Student Performance Checklist:

Read easily without stumbling.

Read with appropriate phrasing and pausing.

Read with appropriate expression for the selection.

Read at a good pace, not too fast and not too slow.

Read to be heard and understood.

Teacher Notes:

Name:

Handout 20B: Fluency Homework Option C

Directions: Practice reading the passage daily for homework. Have an adult initial the bottom after you have done the reading.

In the fall, many things are changing. In many places, there is a change in the weather. There are changes in light and temperature. Inside the leaves, there will be many changes too. All of these changes bring about the beautiful colors of fall.

44 words

Maestro, Betsy. *Why Do Leaves Change Color?* New York: HarperCollins, 1994. 12. Print.

Have an adult initial each day that you read the passage three to five times. Optional: Have a peer sign on the second row of boxes, checking your progress.

Day 1	Day 2	Day 3	Day 4

Student Performance Checklist:

Read easily without stumbling.

Read with appropriate phrasing and pausing.

Read with appropriate expression for the selection.

Read at a good pace, not too fast and not too slow.

Read to be heard and understood.

Teacher Notes:

Name:

Handout 20B: Fluency Homework Option D

Directions: Practice reading the passage daily for homework. Have an adult initial the bottom after you have done the reading.

In the fall, there are fewer hours of sunlight each day. The change in light tells the tree to get ready for winter. Winter is a time of rest for the tree. When winter comes, the tree will have to survive with less water and sunlight.

46 words

Maestro, Betsy. *Why Do Leaves Change Color?* New York: HarperCollins, 1994. 12. Print.

Have an adult initial each day that you read the passage three to five times. Optional: Have a peer sign on the second row of boxes, checking your progress.

Day 1	Day 2	Day 3	Day 4

Student Performance Checklist:

Read easily without stumbling.

Read with appropriate phrasing and pausing.

Read with appropriate expression for the selection.

Read at a good pace, not too fast and not too slow.

Read to be heard and understood.

Teacher Notes:

Name:

Handout 20B: Fluency Homework Option E

Directions: Practice reading the passage daily for homework. Have an adult initial the bottom after you have done the reading.

When the leaves die, they will fall from the tree. This will happen slowly over a number of weeks. As the leaves begin to separate from the tree, they get less water. Without water, the leaves cannot make new chlorophyll. The old chlorophyll begins to fade. The green color starts to disappear.

Now, other colors can be seen in the leaves. Other pigments have been in the leaves all along. But they were hidden by the dark green of the chlorophyll. Once the green color fades, the yellow and orange pigments can be seen.

94 words

Maestro, Betsy. *Why Do Leaves Change Color?* New York: HarperCollins, 1994. 15–16. Print.

Have an adult initial each day that you read the passage three to five times. Optional: Have a peer sign on the second row of boxes, checking your progress.

Day 1	Day 2	Day 3	Day 4

Student Performance Checklist:

Read easily without stumbling.

Read with appropriate phrasing and pausing.

Read with appropriate expression for the selection.

Read at a good pace, not too fast and not too slow.

Read to be heard and understood.

Teacher Notes:

Name:

Handout 21A: Details Collection Strips

Cut on dotted lines. Distribute multiple strips to each group.

	Page #	Detail
	Page #	Detail
	Page #	Detail
	Page #	Detail
	Page #	Detail
	Page #	Detail

Name:

Handout 21B: Topic Sentences and Details

Directions: Cut on dotted lines, then place the topic sentences and details in the appropriate sections of the table.

Exemplar 1

Finally, it's time to jump into the piles of leaves.

Fall leaves create opportunities for work and play.

Working and playing with leaves can be fun.

First, the leaves fall off the trees.

Then it's time to rake the leaves.

Exemplar 2

Squirrels collect food for winter.

In fall some animals get ready for cold weather.

With this stored food, they will have enough food for the winter.

They hide nuts and acorns.

Fall is a busy time for squirrels.

Name:

Handout 22A: Key Word Investigation Charts

Directions: Identify the details about chlorophyll from page 9 of *Why Do Leaves Change Color?* and add these details to the chart. Then answer the question at the bottom of the chart, "Why is chlorophyll important for trees?"

Chlorophyll, page 9

Details

Why is chlorophyll important for trees?

Directions: Identify the details about Leaves from page 11 of *Why Do Leaves Change Color?* and add these details to the chart. Then answer the question at the bottom of the chart, "Why are leaves important for trees?"

Leaves, page 11

Details

Why are leaves important for trees?

Name:

Directions: Identify the details about change from page 12 of *Why Do Leaves Change Color?* and add these details to the chart. Then answer the question at the bottom of the chart, "Why is change important for trees?"

Change, page 12

Details

Why is change important for trees?

Directions: Identify the details about sunlight from pages 9–13 of *Why Do Leaves Change Color?* and add these details to the chart. Then answer the question at the bottom of the chart, "Why is sunlight important for trees?"

Sunlight, pages 9–13

Details

Why is sunlight important for trees?

Name:

Directions: Identify the details about water from page 15 of *Why Do Leaves Change Color?* and add these details to the chart. Then answer the question at the bottom of the chart, "Why is water important for trees?"

Water, page 15
Details

Why is water important for trees?

Directions: Identify the details about pigment from page 16 of *Why Do Leaves Change Color?* and add these details to the chart. Then answer the question at the bottom of the chart, "Why is pigment important for trees?"

Pigment, page 16

Details

Why is pigment important for trees?

Name:

Handout 22B: Change Cards

Directions: Cut on the dotted lines. Then place each card in correct order on the chart.

Summer Sunset

chlorophyll

temperature

pigments

FINALLY	
THEN	
FIRST	

Name: _____

Handout 22C: Multiple-Choice Questions

Directions: Read the sentences carefully. Use what you know about fall to answer the questions.

- When winter comes, the tree will have to *survive* with less water and sunlight.

- Evergreen trees, like pines and spruces, keep their leaves all year. But in cool climates, other trees must lose their leaves to *survive* in winter.

1. *Survive* means:

   a. Become extinct.
   b. Stay alive.
   c. Create new trees.
   d. Provide shelter for birds that do not migrate.

- The best leaf colors *usually* come with lots of bright sunshine and crisp, clear nights.

- Only some places, such as New England, have displays of many colors. This is because the weather conditions there are *usually* just right and there are so many different kinds of trees.

1. *Usually* means:

    a. Most often; most of the time.

    b. Never.

    c. In the daytime.

    d. Weather.

Name:

Handout 23A: Word Link-Up

Directions: Cut apart word cards.

chlorophyll	water
leaves	pigments
change	sunlight
temperature	separate
green	yellow
orange	absorb

Name:

Directions: Record as many Link-Up connections for words as you can.

Record Your Link-Up!

Which two words?	How are these words connected?

Name:

Which four words?	How are these words connected?

Which eight words?	How are these words connected?

Name:

ALL words!	How are these words connected?

Name:

Handout 23B: Informative Paragraph Cards

Directions: Cut the cards apart and use during the oral rehearsals of your informative paragraph.

Topic Statement	Evidence
Evidence	Evidence
Conclusion	

Name:

Handout 23C: Conjunction Review

Directions: Read each of the sentences. Circle the conjunction and explain what it means in the sentence. If you finish early, write a compound sentence using the conjunction *but*.

I like summer, but fall can be fun, too.
We pick apples in fall, and my mother makes pies.
We grow during the summer, so we need new shoes for school.
The weather will get colder, so we'll wear sweaters or jackets.
Birds will fly south, and leaves will fall from the trees.
Birds will fly south, and leaves will fall from the trees

Name: _____

Handout 23D: Mix and Mingle Compound Sentence Cards

Directions: Cut apart the cards.

Trees need sun to make food.	Trees need sun to make food.	Trees need sun to make food.
The green color fades.	The green color fades.	The green color fades.
The tree needs very little food.	The tree needs very little food.	The tree needs very little food.
There is less sun during autumn.	There is less sun during autumn.	There is less sun during autumn.
The leaves stop their work.	The leaves stop their work.	The leaves stop their work.
Yellow and orange pigments can be seen.	Yellow and orange pigments can be seen.	Yellow and orange pigments can be seen.

Name: _____

Leaves begin to separate from the tree.	Leaves begin to separate from the tree.	Leaves begin to separate from the tree.
They get less water.	They get less water.	They get less water.
but	but	but
so	so	so
so	so	so
and	and	and

Name:

Handout 24A: Informative Writing Checklist

Directions: Complete this checklist after completing your informative paragraph. Mark + for "yes" and Δ for "not yet." Be sure to include a writing goal.

Grade 2 Informative Writing Checklist		
	Self +/ Δ	Teacher +/ Δ
Reading Comprehension		
I understand how weather impacts leaves in fall.		
Structure		
I introduce the topic with a topic statement.		
I include at least three sentences with evidence.		
I use sequencing words: *first*, *then*, and *finally* in the correct order.		
I conclude the paragraph with a conclusion.		
Development		
My evidence relates to the topic and helps develop my points.		
Style		
I use words that are about the topic.		
I use simple and compound sentences.		

I combine sentences using *and, but, so.*		
Conventions		
Each of my sentences has one or more subject and verb.		
Total # of checks		

My writing goal is_____

_____

_____

Teacher Feedback

Name:

Handout 25A: Notice and Wonder Chart

Directions: Jot down observations and questions about *Sky Tree* in the Notice and Wonder columns.

Notice	**Wonder**
To see or observe	To ask questions

Name:

Handout 25B: Artist's Colors

Directions: Use crayons to color the palette and show what colors the artist used in the painting.

I added the color_____

because_____

_____

I added the color_____

because_____

_____

I added the color_____

because_____

_____

Why did the artist choose to use those colors?

_____

_____

_____

What season does this painting show?

_____

I added the color_____

because_____

_____

I added the color_____

because_____

_____

Name:

Handout 25C: Fluency Homework Option A

Directions: Practice reading the passage daily for homework. Have an adult initial the bottom after you have done the reading.

Once a tree stood alone on a hill by the river. Through the long days, its leaves fluttered in the soft summer breeze. 23 words Locker, Thomas. *Sky Tree*. New York: HarperCollins, 1995. 4. Print.

Have an adult initial each day that you read the passage three to five times. Optional: Have a peer sign on the second row of boxes, checking your progress.

Day 1	Day 2	Day 3	Day 4

Student Performance Checklist:

Read easily without stumbling.

Read with appropriate phrasing and pausing.

Read with appropriate expression for the selection.

Read at a good pace, not too fast and not too slow.

Read to be heard and understood.

Teacher Notes:

Name:

Handout 25C: Fluency Homework Option B

Directions: Practice reading the passage daily for homework. Have an adult initial the bottom after you have done the reading.

On a gray day, an old snapping turtle buried herself in the river mud, where she would sleep until spring. The tree's bare branches reached toward the sky. The clouds opened, and for a moment, the sky filled the branches.

40 words

Locker, Thomas. *Sky Tree*. New York: HarperCollins, 1995. 4. Print

---

Have an adult initial each day that you read the passage three to five times. Optional: Have a peer sign on the second row of boxes, checking your progress.

Day 1	Day 2	Day 3	Day 4

Student Performance Checklist:

Read easily without stumbling.

Read with appropriate phrasing and pausing.

Read with appropriate expression for the selection.

Read at a good pace, not too fast and not too slow.

Read to be heard and understood.

Teacher Notes:

Name:

Handout 25C: Fluency Homework Option C

Directions: Practice reading the passage daily for homework. Have an adult initial the bottom after you have done the reading.

Snows fell. Snug in their nest, a family of squirrels huddled close through the cold winter days.

At night, millions of stars twinkled among the branches of the tree. Beneath the river ice, the old snapping turtle slept. The world was waiting for spring.

44 words

Locker, Thomas. *Sky Tree*. New York: HarperCollins, 1995. 20. Print

Have an adult initial each day that you read the passage three to five times. Optional: Have a peer sign on the second row of boxes, checking your progress.

Day 1	Day 2	Day 3	Day 4

Student Performance Checklist:

Read easily without stumbling.

Read with appropriate phrasing and pausing.

Read with appropriate expression for the selection.

Read at a good pace, not too fast and not too slow.

Read to be heard and understood.

Teacher Notes:

Name:

Handout 25C: Fluency Homework Option D

Directions: Practice reading the passage daily for homework. Have an adult initial the bottom after you have done the reading.

The tree stood on the hill by the river. Once again, its leaves fluttered in the soft summer breeze.
19 words
Locker, Thomas. *Sky Tree*. New York: HarperCollins, 1995. 30. Print

Have an adult initial each day that you read the passage three to five times. Optional: Have a peer sign on the second row of boxes, checking your progress.

Day 1	Day 2	Day 3	Day 4

Student Performance Checklist:

Read easily without stumbling.

Read with appropriate phrasing and pausing.

Read with appropriate expression for the selection.

Read at a good pace, not too fast and not too slow.

Read to be heard and understood.

Teacher Notes:

Name:

Handout 26A: Revision Paragraph

Directions: Draw arrows to show where the Sentences to Add belong in the Draft Paragraph so all of the sentences make one informative paragraph.

Question: How do changing seasons impact the leaves of deciduous trees?

Draft Paragraph
In the spring and summer, trees grow green leaves. Trees do not have any leaves in the winter. Trees' leaves change with the seasons.

Sentences to Add
The leaves on trees change in every season.
In the autumn, the leaves change color and fall off.

Name:

Handout 27A: Sky Tree Timeline

Directions: Read *Sky Tree* with attention to key details. Write key details under each season as you read.

Summer ⟶	Autumn ⟶	Winter ⟶

Spring ⟶	Summer	

Name:

Handout 27B: Revision Paragraph and Checklist

Directions: Using the Informative Writing Checklist below, revise the Draft Paragraph. On the checklist, mark + for "yes" and Δ for "not yet."

Question: How does the river change in *Sky Tree*?

Draft Paragraph:

First, ice forms at the river's edges in autumn. Then, winter ice and snow cover the river. The river's water changes as temperatures change with the seasons.

Informative Writing Checklist	
	Self +/ Δ
Structure	
I introduce the topic with a topic statement.	
I include at least three sentences with evidence.	
I conclude the paragraph with a conclusion.	
Total # of check's	

Name:

Handout 28A: Season Trees

Directions: Using details from *Sky Tree* and from the Sky Tree Timeline, illustrate one of the trees and add details from the text.

SUMMER TREE

SPRING TREE

Name:

AUTUMN TREE

WINTER TREE

Name:

Handout 28B: Matching Key Terms

Directions: Read through each of the sentences, words and definitions with your team. Match the correct word, definition, and season with each sentence.

"Through the long days, its leaves ---------- in the soft breeze."		
Word	Definition	Season

"Snug in their nest, a family of squirrels ------- close through the cold winter days."		
Word	Definition	Season

"The tree's leaves --------- in the spring sunlight, and the birds returned to build nests for their young."		
Word	Definition	Season

"On a grey day, an old snapping turtle ------- herself in the river mud, where she would sleep until spring."

Word	Definition	Season

"Squirrels -------- to store nuts and acorns."

Word	Definition	Season

"The world was -------- for spring."

word	definition	season

"Late one afternoon, a golden light --------- through the clouds and warmed the tree."

word	definition	season

Name:

Directions: *Cut on the dotted lines and mix up the words, definitions, and seasons.*

fluttered	to move lightly	summer
hurried	to move quickly	fall
buried	to cover something that is in the ground with dirt	fall
huddled	to move close together when sharing something such as heat	winter

Name:

streamed	a continuous flow of something	spring
waiting	when a person stays in one place until some expected event happens	winter
uncurled	to open or straighten	spring

Name: _____

Handout 29A: Informative Paragraph Parts Cards

Directions: Cut the cards apart and use during the oral rehearsals of your informative paragraph.

Topic Statement	Evidence
Evidence	Evidence
Evidence	Evidence
Evidence	Conclusion

Name:

Handout 29B: Informative Writing Checklist

Directions: Complete this checklist after completing your informative paragraph. Mark + for "yes" and Δ for "not yet." Be sure to include a writing goal.

Grade 2 Informative Writing Checklist			
	Self +/ Δ	Peer +/ Δ	Teacher +/ Δ
Reading Comprehension			
I understand how changes in fall impact plants or animals.			
Structure			
I introduce the topic with a topic statement.			
I include at least three sentences with evidence.			
I use sequencing words: *first, then,* and *finally* in the correct order.			
I conclude the paragraph with a conclusion.			
Development			
My evidence relates to the topic and helps develop my points.			

Style			
I use words that are about the topic.			
I use adjectives to describe setting, story, or characters.			
I use simple and compound sentences.			
I combine sentences using *and, but, so*.			
Conventions			
Each of my sentences has one or more subject and verb.			
Total # of check's			

My writing goal is_____

_____

_____

Teacher Feedback

Name: _____

Handout 30A: Evidence Organizer

Directions: Add information from the two texts to the chart below to provide evidence of changes in weather and the impact on people.

Practice Question: How do changes in weather impact people in fall?		
	Text 1:	Text 2:
Change in Weather		
Impact on People		

Name:

Handout 31A: Informative Writing Checklist

Directions: Complete this checklist after completing your informative paragraph. Mark + for "yes" and Δ for "not yet." Be sure to include a writing goal.

Grade 2 Informative Writing Checklist	Self +/ Δ	Peer +/ Δ	Teacher +/ Δ
Reading Comprehension			
I show the impact of changes in fall weather on plants or animals.			
Structure			
I introduce the topic with a topic statement.			
I include at least three sentences with evidence.			
I use evidence from two texts.			
I conclude the paragraph with a conclusion.			
Development			
My evidence relates to the topic and helps develop my points.			

Style			
I use words that are about the topic.			
I use simple and compound sentences.			
I combine sentences using *and, but, so.*			
Conventions			
Each of my sentences has one or more subject and verb.			
Total # of check's			

My writing goal is_____

_____

_____

Teacher Feedback

Name:

Handout 31B: Evidence Organizer

Directions: Use this Evidence Organizer to answer the question: "How do changes in weather impact plants or animals in fall?" to plan for the End-of Module Task.

Practice Question: How do changes in weather impact plants or animals in fall?		
	Text 1:	**Text 2:**
Change in Weather		
Impact on Plants		
Impact on Animals		

Name: _____

Volume of Reading Reflection Questions

Directions: Share your knowledge about weather and seasonal changes by responding or sharing one question in each category below.

A *Season of Change*, Grade 2, Module 1

Text:

Author:

Topic:

Genre/type of book:

1. Wonder: Why did you choose to read this text about the seasons or the different types of changes that take place in nature?

2. Wonder: What do you notice and wonder about the text you selected?

3. Wonder: What kind of text did you choose? Is it a story, poem, informational, or something else? What details do you notice about the text that give you clues to the way that the author presents the story?

4. Organize: What parts of the text were hard to understand? What vocabulary did you find tricky?

5. Organize: What's happening in the text? Use a routine like Story Stones (setting, character, problem, solution) or Buttons and Bags to recount or describe what happened in the text. First recount or describe the text to a friend. Then write it down.

6. Organize: What changes happen to the main character throughout the text? Draw or illustrate an important event that happen to this character during the story.

7. Reveal: What is one important idea that the author wants you to learn about the seasons or nature? Choose a sentence or illustration in the book that shows this important idea.

8. Distill: What message or theme did the author want you to learn by reading this book? Find the page or line that most strongly communicates that message.

9. Distill: How did the main character change in the book from the beginning to the end of the story? Draw two pictures of the character. One picture showing the character "before" the change, and one showing "after" the change.

10. Know: What surprising or new information did you learn by reading this book? What new ideas about the changes that happen in nature or the seasons did you learn?

11. Know: How does this text connect to the other texts about nature or the changing of seasons we have read or ideas we have discussed in this module?

WIT & WISDOM PARENT TIP SHEET

WHAT IS MY SECOND GRADE STUDENT LEARNING IN MODULE 1?

Wit & Wisdom is our English curriculum. It builds knowledge of key topics in history, science, and literature through the study of excellent texts. By reading and responding to stories and nonfiction texts, we will build knowledge of the following topics:

Module 1: A Season of Change

Module 2: American West

Module 3: Civil Rights Heroes

Module 4: Good Eating

In this first module, A *Season of Change*, we will study how the world changes every season. We will observe the colors, textures, and causes in the cycle of the seasons and consider paintings of rainy, sunny, and snow-covered landscapes. We will discover how change affects us all.

OUR CLASS WILL READ THESE BOOKS:

Picture Books (Informational)

- *How Do You Know It's Fall?*, Lisa M. Herrington
- *Why Do Leaves Change Color?*, Betsy Maestro

Picture Books (Literary)

- *The Little Yellow Leaf*, Carin Berger
- *A Color of His Own*, Leo Lionni
- *Sky Tree*, Thomas Locker

Poems

- "Weather," Eve Merriam

OUR CLASS WILL EXAMINE THESE PAINTINGS:

- *Autumn Landscape*, Maurice de Vlaminck
- *Bathers at Asnières*, Georges Seurat

- *Hunters in the Snow*, Pieter Bruegel the Elder
- *Paris Street, Rainy Day*, Gustave Caillebotte

OUR CLASS WILL ASK THESE QUESTIONS:

- What changes in "Weather"?
- How do changes in fall weather impact people and nature?
- How does the Little Yellow Leaf change?
- How does the chameleon change?
- How does weather impact leaves in fall?
- How does *Sky Tree* show the cycle of seasons?
- How does change impact people and nature?

QUESTIONS TO ASK AT HOME:

As you read with your second grade student, ask:

- *What do you notice and wonder?*

BOOKS TO READ AT HOME:

- *The Longest Day: Celebrating the Summer Solstice*, Wendy Pfeffer
- *The Shortest Day: Celebrating the Winter Solstice*, Wendy Pfeffer
- *Poppleton in Winter*, Cynthia Rylant
- *Frog and Toad All Year*, Arnold Lobel
- *Henry and Mudge in the Sparkle Days*, Cynthia Rylant
- *Snow*, Cynthia Rylant
- *Over and Under the Snow*, Kate Messner

PLACES YOU CAN VISIT TO TALK ABOUT THE SEASONS:

Take a walk in the park together. Ask:

- *What do you notice about the leaves on the trees?*
- *What animals have we seen in the park?*
- *What do you wonder about the animals during this season?*
- *What is your favorite part about being outside during this season?*

CREDITS

Great Minds® has made every effort to obtain permission for the reprinting of all copyrighted material. If any owner of copyrighted material is not acknowledged herein, please contact Great Minds® for proper acknowledgment in all future editions and reprints of this module.

- All material from the *Common Core State Standards for English Language Arts & Literacy in History/Social Studies, Science, and Technical Subjects* © Copyright 2010 National Governors Association Center for Best Practices and Council of Chief State School Officers. All rights reserved.

- All images are used under license from Shutterstock.com unless otherwise noted.

- For updated credit information, please visit **http://witeng.link/credits**.

ACKNOWLEDGMENTS

Great Minds® Staff

The following writers, editors, reviewers, and support staff contributed to the development of this curriculum.

Ann Brigham, Lauren Chapalee, Sara Clarke, Emily Climer, Lorraine Griffith, Emily Gula, Sarah Henchey, Trish Huerster, Stephanie Kane-Mainier, Lior Klirs, Liz Manolis, Andrea Minich, Lynne Munson, Marya Myers, Rachel Rooney, Aaron Schifrin, Danielle Shylit, Rachel Stack, Sarah Turnage, Michelle Warner, Amy Wierzbicki, Margaret Wilson, and Sarah Woodard.

Colleagues and Contributors

We are grateful for the many educators, writers, and subject-matter experts who made this program possible.

David Abel, Robin Agurkis, Elizabeth Bailey, Julianne Barto, Amy Benjamin, Andrew Biemiller, Charlotte Boucher, Sheila Byrd-Carmichael, Jessica Carloni, Eric Carey, Janine Cody, Rebecca Cohen, Elaine Collins, Tequila Cornelious, Beverly Davis, Matt Davis, Thomas Easterling, Jeanette Edelstein, Kristy Ellis, Moira Clarkin Evans, Charles Fischer, Marty Gephart, Kath Gibbs, Natalie Goldstein, Christina Gonzalez, Mamie Goodson, Nora Graham, Lindsay Griffith, Brenna Haffner, Joanna Hawkins, Elizabeth Haydel, Steve Hettleman, Cara Hoppe, Ashley Hymel, Carol Jago, Jennifer Johnson, Mason Judy, Gail Kearns, Shelly Knupp, Sarah Kushner, Shannon Last, Suzanne Lauchaire, Diana Leddy, David Liben, Farren Liben, Jennifer Marin, Susannah Maynard, Cathy McGath, Emily McKean, Jane Miller, Rebecca Moore, Cathy Newton, Turi Nilsson, Julie Norris, Galemarie Ola, Michelle Palmieri, Meredith Phillips, Shilpa Raman, Tonya Romayne, Emmet Rosenfeld, Jennifer Ruppel, Mike Russoniello, Deborah Samley, Casey Schultz, Renee Simpson, Rebecca Sklepovich, Amelia Swabb, Kim Taylor, Vicki Taylor, Melissa Thomson, Lindsay Tomlinson, Melissa Vail, Keenan Walsh, Julia Wasson, Lynn Welch, Yvonne Guerrero Welch, Emily Whyte, Lynn Woods, and Rachel Zindler.

Early Adopters

The following early adopters provided invaluable insight and guidance for Wit & Wisdom:

- Bourbonnais School District 53 • Bourbonnais, IL
- Coney Island Prep Middle School • Brooklyn, NY
- Gate City Charter School for the Arts • Merrimack, NH
- Hebrew Academy for Special Children • Brooklyn, NY
- Paris Independent Schools • Paris, KY
- Saydel Community School District • Saydel, IA
- Strive Collegiate Academy • Nashville, TN
- Valiente College Preparatory Charter School • South Gate, CA
- Voyageur Academy • Detroit, MI

Design Direction provided by Alton Creative, Inc.

Project management support, production design, and copyediting services provided by ScribeConcepts.com

Copyediting services provided by Fine Lines Editing

Product management support provided by Sandhill Consulting